Also by James Campbell and Rob Jones

THE FUNNY LIFE OF SHARKS

HELLO!

Side-splittingly funny

CAUTION! Not to be used for homework

JAMES CAMPBELL

ROB JONES

Will have you fart-chuckling so much your shoes will fly off

A really good (as long...

BLOOMSBURY

'We laughed so much we woke the baby.'
Saskia, aged 39,
Jakob, aged 5

'James Campbell is the funniest man I know. Read this book to your cat!' – Chris Riddell

THE FUNNY LIFE OF PETS

Pants-wettingly funny

CAUTION! Not to be used for homework!

JAMES CAMPBELL

ROB JONES

The funniest man alive (according to his mum)

Really good at drawing dogs (according to his cat)

BLOOMSBURY

'Deliciously delightful. Superbly epic and funnier than any other book I've read.'
Ethan, aged 9

This book is dedicated to all the children who took writing workshops with me throughout lockdown. We kept each other going with stories and silliness, through a time we'll never forget.

So many thanks to Layla, Josie, Lizzie, Beaumont, Fin, Alexander, Daniel, Oscar, Holly, Hazel, Harrison, Wilf, Amber, Thomas, Erin, Melissa, Mark, Danny, Kezzy, Logan, Berys, Bill, Leo, Joseph, Amelia, Isabel, Lilly, Matthias, Izzy, Nellie, Charlotte, Sam, Samson, Hannah, Dora, Gray, Mags, Laura, Olivia and Henry – James Campbell

In loving memory of my first teacher,
Mrs. Rush – Rob Jones

BLOOMSBURY CHILDREN'S BOOKS
Bloomsbury Publishing Plc
50 Bedford Square, London, WC1B 3DP, UK
29 Earlsfort Terrace, Dublin 2

BLOOMSBURY, BLOOMSBURY CHILDREN'S BOOKS and the Diana logo
are trademarks of Bloomsbury Publishing Plc
First published in Great Britain 2021 by Bloomsbury Publishing Plc
Text copyright © James Campbell, 2021
Illustrations copyright © Rob Jones, 2021
Typeset by Janene Spencer

James Campbell and Rob Jones have asserted their rights under the Copyright, Designs
and Patents Act, 1988, to be identified as Author and Illustrator of this work

A catalogue record for this book is available from the British Library

ISBN: PB: 978-1-4088-8365-5

2 4 6 8 10 9 7 5 3 1

Printed and bound in Great Britain by CPI (UK) Ltd, Croydon CR0 4YY

To find out more about our authors and books visit www.bloomsbury.com
and sign up for our newsletters

The author and publisher recommend enabling SafeSearch when using the Internet in conjunction with this book. We can accept no responsibility for information published on the Internet.

Write YOUR OWN FUNNY Stories

JAMES CAMPBELL

ROB JONES

BLOOMSBURY
CHILDREN'S BOOKS
LONDON OXFORD NEW YORK NEW DELHI SYDNEY

WELCOME TO THE INSIDE OF THE BOOK.

I just want to let you know that this is absolutely NOT A NORMAL BOOK!

If you're looking for a normal book then put this one down immediately and then train **a labradoodle** to take the book away, bury it under a tree and then decorate the tree with weird furry things that it has found from between the dishwasher and the washing machine.

Take a flick through the pages. You'll notice that there is no right or wrong way to read this book. You can read it in any order. You might also notice that some of the pages have nothing on them at all. Those pages are for you to write in. How often do you get to do that?

You CAN read this book from the beginning and make your way to the end if you like but you could also pick a bit in the middle that you like the look of and start there. The whole book is full of different **tips, tricks and activities** to help you write your own funny story.

If at any point though, you think to yourself ...

I think I'm just going to use this page to draw a really cool picture of a marmot and then see how many different words I can think of to use instead of BUM

... then that's fine.

Why don't you do that, take a picture of it and then email the picture. My address is:

stopsendingmeweirdpicturesofmarmots@whatever.com

If you're reading this book, you probably like writing. You might even want to be an **author** when you grow up. So what are you waiting for? Why wait until you grow up? Why not start now? Get a notebook. Do some writing. **Be a writer.**

If you're thinking to yourself, 'I've written lots of stuff, I write in notebooks all the time!' then that's **brilliant**. In that case you already are an author. Don't tell people you want to be an author when you grow up. Tell them you are an author **now**. In fact, more importantly, tell yourself that you are an author now.

As far as I can see, the biggest difference between someone who is an author and someone who isn't an author is that an author **writes stuff.**

So if you want to be an author all you need to do is get on with it. Why wait until you're older? It's not like you need a driving licence. You don't have to be a certain height. For most jobs you need to be a **grown-up** before you can start. You can't be an astronaut until you are an adult. If you want to

YOU MUST BE THIS TALL TO BE AN ASTRONAUT.

be Prime Minister you have to wait until you grow up. If you want to be a hairdresser, no one will let you cut their hair until you are bigger.

However, if you want to do some writing you can start **right now**. All you need is a pen and notebook. (And this book might help too).

WARMING UP THE MACHINE

This is just a little exercise to get you warmed up for writing your own story. A bit like doing some **stretches** before playing football or jogging on the spot for ten minutes before climbing and falling off an elephant.

What I would like you to do first is think of a **magical machine**. It can do anything you want. Go crazy with it. Maybe it makes people invisible or turns ducks into ice cream. If nothing springs to mind just think of something you really like. Your machine makes whatever that thing is.

Use the space below to draw a picture of your machine.
What does it look like? Is it big like a truck or tiny like a watch?
Is it metal or plastic? Is it big and dirty like a tractor
or clean and polished like a phone?

Next think about where your machine came from. How did it come into your life? Did your mum teach you how to use it? Did a strange uncle you've never seen before turn up one birthday and give you the machine? Did you find your machine? Did it fall out of the sky? Did you build it out of material you found in the rubbish dump?

Use the space below to describe where you got your machine:

I got my machine
from asda

Use the space below to describe what your machine does:

My machine Fires Snowballs
out of a Tube.

Now think about the day something went wrong with the machine. Tell yourself about the time someone pressed the wrong button or put the wrong thing in the machine. Maybe you didn't listen to the instructions. Or maybe the people you got it from want it back. Use the space below to describe this:

My machine is if you
Press 90 2 times it
will explode

Ending your story here might not be **satisfying** for your reader. It might be a good idea to have some sort of **resolution** at the end, some way of making things better.

Use the space below to describe this:

Now, with a bit of **tweaking** you should find that you have just created a whole story. You won't have written everything that happens, of course, but you should have a **beginning, middle and end**, which is like the skeleton of a story – the bones that hold it all together.

The beginning is how you got your machine.

The middle is what it does.

The end is when it all goes horribly wrong.

And **the final section** is the resolution.

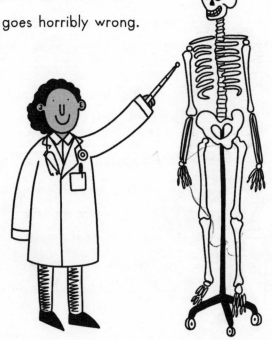

Below is an example of a **skeleton of a story**:

One day I found a machine in the school art cupboard. After a bit of fiddling about I found it was a machine for turning snails into candyfloss.

I had lots of fun using the machine until one day the king and queen of the snails turned up at my house and ate my carpets in **revenge** for what I had done to all of their snail friends.

After a lot of fiddling around and pressing buttons I worked out how to reverse the effects of the machine and turn the candyfloss back into snails. This made the king and queen of the snails feel a lot better about the whole thing and we all lived happily ever after. Without any carpets.

Are you pleased with your story? Hopefully you are but this is not the story you are going to write. That would be too easy. The story you are going to write is going to be the best story you have ever written.

But you're not going to start writing straight away. First you need to **think of some ideas**, plan those ideas and organise your thoughts.

Writing a story without planning it first would be like eating your dinner without opening your mouth, trying to watch a TV programme without switching on the TV, or going to school without getting dressed first.

Pull your socks up, grab a sandwich and a glass of water and **let's get started!**

IDEAS

Welcome to the **ideas section**. This is where you're going to get started on working out what you're going to write about.

This section is about ideas because without an idea you can't write a story. You can know all the **tools** for writing in the world. You can know about story mountains, story roller coasters, mind maps, wow words and great openers but if you haven't got an idea for the story, you have nothing to write.

You need an idea to write your story. Where is it going to come from? Where do ideas come from? Some people think that ideas are made **inside** our brains while others think that ideas form **outside** of our heads and then go into our brains. I think it's a mixture of the two.

Before I started writing properly, I used to think that writers would get the **whole idea** for a book in their head all at that same time. Like in one big whoosh.

But the more I write, the more I realise that isn't true for me. Maybe it works like that for some people but what happens in my world is that I might get a little bit of an idea – or maybe even just half an idea – and then I either put it in my notebook or on the noticeboard inside my head. Then a couple of days later I might notice something else or hear a **funny phrase**. And then I'll connect up the two ideas in my head or on paper and then I'll try and make it grow.

Use the space below and on the next page to write down where you think your ideas come from:

_____

_____

_____

_____

_____

_____

The Inspiration Elf

It's a lot easier to write a story if you have a **brilliant idea**, and writing should be easy, not hard!

So where do authors get all their ideas from? No one really knows where ideas come from – lots of writers find their ideas come when they start writing. I think that ideas are out there waiting for everyone but you have to be working on something to catch them. Maybe if we imagine that inspiration is some sort of person or creature – let's call it the **Inspiration Elf**.

This magical creature travels around the world with a big sack of ideas. They are ideas for stories, poems, paintings, sculptures, games, films, recipes, treehouses, plays and anything else that needs an idea to **get started**.

Use the space below to write a list of things you might need an idea for. Take some time to imagine what you think the Inspiration Elf might look like. You can describe the Inspiration Elf or draw it in the space below if you like.

The Inspiration Elf really wants people to have ideas but there is one condition. It has to find you writing or at least trying to. If it looks through your window and finds you watching TV or staring into space then it won't be keen to give you any of the contents of its bountiful **sack of ideas**. Why would it? You don't look like you want to be a writer and it will simply pass on to the next window and find someone else to inspire.

If, however, when the Inspiration Elf comes calling, it finds you doing something — holding a pen or pencil in your hand, hovering over a notepad or with a paintbrush sketching out ideas — then it will empty all of its ideas on your desk and let you **choose** the one that suits you best.

Try this exercise to see if the Inspiration Elf is looking through your window. Start writing something and see what happens. It doesn't matter what you write. It doesn't even have to make any sense!

Below are some sentences to get you started:

For breakfast today I ate ...

_____

_____

_____

_____

_____

_____

If I had a magic shoe I would ...

_____

_____

_____

_____

_____

_____

If I was president of the world, the first thing I would do is ...

_____

_____

_____

_____

_____

_____

I can't think of anything to write about. If I had a brilliant idea
I would be really happy about it because ...

_____

_____

_____

_____

_____

_____

Boredom

Ideas can also spring to mind when someone is **really bored**. This might be because the Inspiration Elf is trying to deliver so many ideas that the only time it can deliver them is when your brain is relaxed and doing something that doesn't use a lot of effort. Something boring.

Use the space below to write down why you don't like being bored. What does it feel like? What happens inside your head when you are bored?

People are often **afraid** of being bored. The world has been designed to stop us from being bored and parents are very careful not to let their children get bored. This is because they're worried you might have ideas. Not ideas for stories. Ideas like:

'Today I am going to redecorate my bedroom – using mayonnaise.'
'I'm going to experiment and find a new way to go to the toilet.'

'I'm going to make a suit of armour for the dog
and make it stay on – with glue.'

My own experience of being bored is that it can be an important part of the creative process. It's the gap before something wonderful happens. Let me give you an example:

You know when you're on a long car journey and the iPad is out of charge and it's going to be another three hours until you get to where you are going and you are bored. Properly eye-hurting bored. You start looking out of the window and think to yourself, 'I wonder what's in that lorry? Maybe it's full of monkeys. I wonder where the monkeys are going? Maybe they're going on holiday. Where do monkeys go on holiday? Some sort of Monkey Land.'

And then you might think, because you're a writer, 'Ooh. Monkey Land. That might be a good idea for a story.'

When you are on your own and you don't know what to do and you are bored you start looking at things in a different way. You look at a tree and ask yourself, 'I wonder if that tree ever goes on holiday. If it could just pull up its roots and go for a walk where would it go? Maybe it goes to the same place as the monkeys. Maybe the monkeys climb on the tree and the tree loves being climbed on because it tickles. That's a really **good idea** for a story.'

Next time you are **bored** – before you reach for the remote control or the games console – do this exercise. Sit still and say to yourself, 'I am bored.' Then ask yourself, 'What will I think next?' And then listen to what you think next. What did you think? Is it an idea for a story?

Write any thoughts or story ideas in the space below:

Talking to **boring people** can also be a great way to get ideas. You know when somebody starts telling you something really boring and you're supposed to be listening but you just can't and suddenly you find your mind starts wandering off ...

I wonder how many monkeys it would take to make a mountain? If you had a million monkeys in a **massive pile** would that be a mountain of monkeys? Or maybe if all the trees that have gone to Monkey Land on holiday stood on top of each other's shoulders in a mountain-sized pyramid and then all the monkeys climbed onto the trees and squashed themselves together so that the trees were entirely covered in monkeys. Then one day you would see this mountain in the distance and it would look just like an ordinary mountain and you would decide to climb that mountain, but as you walked closer to it you would begin to notice that there was something very unusual about this mountain because it looks to be furry and ... it's moving!

Then you'd get right up to it and realise that this mountain was made out of monkeys and there would be monkey faces and monkey tails and monkey bottoms and you would realise you'd stumbled upon a **monkey mountain**. But then some of the monkeys would move to one side to let you see into the mountain and you would get out your torch and you would carefully climb inside Monkey Mountain and realise that inside the mountain was made up of thousands of trees all standing on top of each other and you would decide to explore this strange, under-monkey tree world and see what you could find.'

Now that's a **great idea** for a story!

The important thing to remember is that ideas and inspiration seem to come from all sorts of places in all sorts of ways and at all sorts of times. If you can put some **effort** into having ideas using these techniques then you will soon become better at having brilliant ideas.

You're probably already getting better at having ideas just from getting **this far** in the book.

Playing

That's **enough** of being bored.

What about ideas that are more like playing? What about the ideas you get when you're in the playground or when you're mucking about in the garden at the weekend?

I'm convinced that **writing** and **playing** are very similar things. Maybe writing is just playing games but with a pen. Is it possible that stories are just games that we take the time to write down?

You know when you're standing in the playground minding your own business and your friend jumps in front of you and shouts, 'I'm a **dragon**!'

He's got his arms outstretched like menacing wings and he looks like he's about to shoot fire out of his face. What do you do?

You might say, 'I'm a dragon too. Let's fly around the playground and set fire to things with our mouths.' Or you might make sure your tights are on straight and then say, 'Well I'm a princess and I like to have dragons as pets. I'm going to put a spell on you and you will have to do what I tell you to – **FOREVER!**'

Or maybe they will say, 'I'm a dragon', and you will say, 'Well I'm a cow.'

'**A** cow?'

'**Y**es. Not any old cow. I'm a **magical cow**. I don't make boring old milk. I make **marmalade**. It comes out of my ears. It's not normal marmalade either.
It's special marmalade and if you set fire to something with your dragon face I can extinguish the flames with my marmalade.'

And then you look
at each other and say,
'Let's play Dragons
and Marmalade Cows!' And you do. And you
make up whole worlds around the idea. Your game gets so good
that it starts to attract other people. Friends want to join in.

Smaller children wander over and
want to play too. You tell
them you are playing Dragons and
Marmalade Cows and they will want
to be Marmalade Cows too,
or Marmite Pigs, or
Lemon Curd Ponies.
Maybe they will pretend to be a
Jammy Hippo!

Next time you are in the playground at school, make an effort to play **imaginative games** with your friends and see what happens. As you line up to go back into the classroom, ask yourself, were there any stories in those games you were playing?

Use the space below and on the next page to try a little experiment. Sit still for as long as it takes for you to realise that you have become bored. Then write whatever comes into your brain. Don't worry about what you're writing or where it's going. Just write. Think of it as a bit like running around outside. You're not running anywhere in particular. You're just running for the sake of it.

_____

_____

_____

_____

_____

_____

Now read back over what you wrote. Are there any **good ideas** for stories in your writing?

By now you should have jotted down lots of ideas for stories. Flick back through the pages you have written on and read your ideas again. They are all nuggets of gold. Take a deep breath – you're ready for the **next step** in your writing adventure.

SHOW ME THE FUNNY!

I am better at writing **funny stories**. (Every now and again I try and write something serious and grown-up and it just sounds weird.) Maybe you can make your story funny too. So how do we do that?

Well the first thing you can do is try and notice funny things when they are happening in **real life**. If something makes you laugh, ask yourself, 'Why is that funny? What is the funny bit? Can I use that in my story?'

It's usually best though not to worry about being funny first of all. Start with a really **good story** and then work out how to make it funny. If your story is like a cake then the funny is the icing on the top. Everyone's favourite bit is the icing but you still need the cake as well, otherwise it's not a cake, it's just a pile of icing. And if you only eat icing you will be sick and your bottom will explode like a dynamitey trumpet.

Funny

The other thing to remember with funny stories is that they don't have to be funny all the time. You can have some straight bits too.

The best way to make your stories funny, though, is to start with the **characters**. If the characters are hilarious they will do hilarious things. Sometimes you just have to imagine them well enough in your head and then watch what they do.

For example: a Marmalade Cow is quite a funny idea on its own because marmalade and cow are not usually words which you find together. But can I make it even **funnier?**

'The Marmalade Cow looked just like an ordinary cow except for the way its nostrils flared into smokey tunnels so big you could drive a minibus up them.'

Maybe you should get yourself a **special notebook**. Quite a small one and keep it in your pocket all the time. Call it your **funny notebook**. Then use it to write down anything that makes you laugh or anything funny that pops into your mind. If nothing funny is happening, you could write a list of things and people you find funny in general. Here are mine for this week:

THINGS THAT MADE ME LAUGH LAST WEEK

1. I closed a gate in the garden for the first time in six months and my dog walked straight into it.

2. I went diving with sharks in Skegness Aquarium and it was only once I was underwater that I remembered you can't talk when you're scuba diving.

3. My daughter, who is called Daphne, pulled a funny face.

4. My wife did an enormous fart. I pretended to be a doctor and said, 'You have a case of the thunderous **bum-trumpets.'**

5. There was a funny line in a TV show I was watching.

THINGS AND PEOPLE I FIND FUNNY:

1. My stepfather always does a funny cough before he tells a story.

2. My dog is usually doing **something funny**.

3. My son often says normal phrases but puts the emphasis on the wrong word. The other day he turned to me and said, 'Daddy. What IS the point?'

4. My friend Ben always makes me laugh (partly because his head is on upside down).

5. The **Shrek** films.

Now use this space to write your list of funny things:

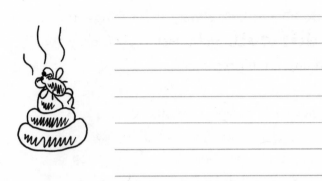

The next thing to do is to have a look at why these things are funny. This can be quite **difficult** and sometimes it's okay for things to simply just be funny for no reason.

But the more you look closely at funny things the more you'll understand about funniness and the funnier your stories will be.

For example, when my son puts the **wrong emphasis** on words in a phrase, it's funny because it takes something that is familiar and makes it mean something different. This is surprising and it makes me laugh.

If I look at my list of things that have made me laugh and things that I find funny in general I can see that what makes these things funny is a **variety** of the following:

- Funny accidents
- Slapstick (which is pretty much the same as funny accidents but can also include doing exaggerated funny things with your body)
- Remembering something you had forgotten
- Not being able to do something you normally can
- Funny faces
- Bodily functions (like farting, sneezing, weeing, pooing, snotting and doing any of these in a toilet on a coach)
- Using funny words
- People with unusual habits
- Love

The last one is quite important I think. Funny things seem to be best when there is love involved. Laughing at something with meanness is not what we're after at all. I laugh at my dog not because I am mean. I laugh at her because she is funny and I love her.

You should now have a pretty good idea of what makes you laugh and why. Maybe these sorts of things should be in your story.

Sometimes you'll get **lucky**. You'll see something funny in real life, and it's so brilliant you can just put it in your story and it'll work.

Usually though, you have to make something funnier or more absurd before it fits in.

So how can we make things **EVEN** funnier?

A simple way to look at this is to think in terms of:

WHO they are

WHAT they are doing

WHY they are doing it

WHERE they are doing it

And then make all those elements funnier in some way.

So my dog walking into a gate is **quite funny**.

If I look at **WHO** the dog is though I could make it funnier by giving the dog a funny name. Like Mrs Soundbyte the Cockapoo.

And **WHAT** they are doing is walking into a gate. But if I changed it to an electric fence that could be **funnier**.

The dog was probably just walking around the garden but if I change the **WHY** she was doing it to something pompous and silly ... and I change the **WHERE** to somewhere in public where everyone could see ... I might get something like:

Mrs Soundbyte the Cockapoo was furious at not being allowed in the school playground so she stomped off to go home but walked straight into the electric fence that the head teacher had installed that morning. She got something of a shock!

44

Use the space below to try to make things funnier.

Think of WHO you know that you find funny (this can be an animal, someone you know, a celebrity or you could make someone up). Now, can you make them even funnier?

_____

_____

_____

_____

_____

_____

Write down WHAT this person/animal could be doing. Can you make this description funnier?

_____

_____

_____

_____

_____

_____

Write down WHY they are doing what they are doing.
Can you change this to something funnier?

_____

_____

_____

_____

_____

_____

Finally, write down WHERE they are doing it ...
and then try to make this funnier.

_____

_____

_____

_____

_____

_____

Funny words

Some words are just funnier than others, even if their meaning isn't actually anything funny.

So think about the words you are using. Could you use a word that means the same but sounds more **hilarious?**

For example:

Margarine is funnier than Butter.

Catapulted is funnier than Flew.

Widdershins is funnier than Anticlockwise.

Bovine Ruminant is funnier than Cow.

Knickers is funnier than Underwear.

Gallivant is funnier than Go for a walk.

Think of some everyday simple words and for each one find a word that means the same but is longer and funnier-sounding. Write your words below:

_____

_____

_____

_____

Generally speaking, the longer and weirder the word is the **funnier** it will be.

There are of course **exceptions**. Sometimes a deliberately plain word is much more funny. Especially at the end of a list of funny things. Like: she had five sisters who were called Bumblina, Thumblina, Whumblina, Chumblina and Paul.

Some of my favourite words are **Bang, Malaysian** and **Scribble**.

But my favourite word in the whole wide world is – **YES**.

Making up new words

It's also fun to make up some **new words**.

I've just made up the word **Bazoopial**. Something is bazoopial when it is so good that it is better than a trip to the zoo.

I've also made up the word **Scrunchwarbling** which means that something is so scary it makes your nose warble.

Make up some new words yourself, write them down here and remember to explain what they mean:

_____

_____

_____

_____

_____

Silly similes

Similes are a **tool** we use in writing to describe something as being like something else. This is really handy if you want to write about something you have made up. For example, if I'm going to write about a made-up creature called a Horken-Zoop, it might be helpful to tell you in the story that a **Horken-Zoop** looks like a unicorn with chickenpox.

Sometimes you might want to describe something as being funny. **Silly similes** are a good way to do this.

If something is as funny as a badger's poo-face, for example, you can use that simile to describe anything.

Similarly, things and people can be smelly as a labrador's armpit; spotty as a leopard's knickers; and tiny as a mouse's pimple.

Why don't you use these pages to make up
some of your own silly similes:

Things you need to be a writer

To do most jobs you need some sort of equipment. Things. **Actual stuff**.

If you want to be a builder you will need tools, bricks, a saw, a hammer, power tools (probably a complete set of Dewalt Cordless 18V lithium-ion drills and drivers).

If you want to be a **hairdresser** you will need scissors, a hairdryer, a comb and an endless interest in other people's holidays.

So if you want to be a writer, what tools will you need? What stuff? What **equipment?**

The first thing you'll need is something to write with. I tend to use a **pen**. Sometimes I use a pencil but I find pencils are really noisy and annoying. I like pens because they are silent and you get to watch the words flow out of them.

You don't need a really expensive pen. It doesn't need to be a Galactic-Unicorn Pen. It doesn't have to be silver or gold or forged in Switzerland from parts of mythical creatures. Just a pen will do.

I do like my pens to write **smoothly** though. Life is too short for scratchy pens that stop working every five minutes. Find yourself a type of pen that does what you want it to.

I tend to buy my pens in packs of five from the supermarket. I put them in a **special place** where no one can find them and then my children find them and steal them! I then chase them around the house while they sing, 'I've got Daddy's pen ... I've got Daddy's pen ...' until I collapse from exhaustion.

In the olden days – when everything was in black and white and smartphones were made out of wood – writers used a special type of feather called a **quill**. I think we should bring this back!

Imagine if in the corner of your classroom at school there wasn't a box full of pens but instead there was a duck! A big fat feathery duck sitting there on a special duck stool. And if you wanted to write a story you'd have to go to the duck and pluck one of its feathers out! That would slow things down a bit. Imagine if everyone wanted to write a story at the same time! You'd end up with a **bald duck!**

And **where** would the ink come from?

Maybe you could have a squid living under your desk in an old washing-up bowl. But how would you get ink out of it? Squids only squirt ink when they are scared or surprised. So every time you wanted ink to write with you'd have to grab hold of the squid and shout **BOO!** at it. With all the squirting and quacking and booing going on no one would be able to concentrate. Thank goodness for pens!

Draw the funniest thing you could use as a pen.
Give it a funny name.

As well as something to write **WITH** you will, of course, need something to write **ON**.

You can write on lots of stuff. Pieces of paper. Notebooks. Walls. Your face. Someone else's face. A cat's bottom. The side of a cow.

Actually **don't** write a story on the side of a cow. Even if the thing stays still for long enough there is a danger that halfway through your story, the cow will get bored or notice a particularly tasty bit of grass and then run away. Then you'll be faced with an awkward conversation with someone. 'Where is that story you were writing?' 'It ran away!' 'Why?' 'It was scared of all the quacking and squirting and booing.'

Write a list of all the funny things you could write on. You could also write down all the places where you have written, like in the car on the way to school, at an aquarium, in a museum ...

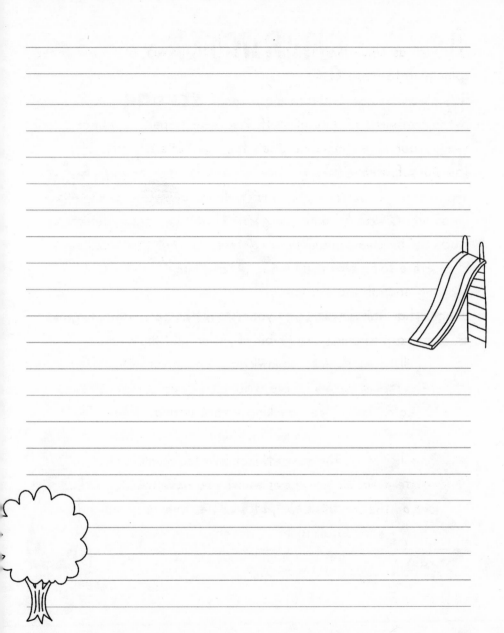

CHARACTERS

It's always a good idea to make really **strong** characters for your story.

And it's always better to have a small number of really interesting characters rather than millions of boring ones. When I was little I wrote a detective story about a gang of detectives made up of every single person in my class. That was 30 characters before I'd even made up a villain.

A **main character** and a **sidekick** is often a good idea. A gang of three usually works well. A villain and his evil assistant is often wonderful.

Try and make sure that all your characters are working really hard for the story. But most of all, make sure they are well rounded and **interesting**, then they will do all sorts of adventurous things that you hadn't thought of.

Here is a list of the main characters in my story:

- The Marmalade Cow
- Daphne the Milkmaid
- Broghainn Laoiugh the Unpronounceable Wizard-Farmer
- A lorry-load of monkeys

Use the space below to make a list of characters you could use in your stories. They could all be made up but you could also borrow some people from real life!

Who are your characters?

Use the space below and on the next page to draw some of your characters.

Then add labels around your drawings explaining their likes/dislikes, hobbies, favourite colour, favourite food etc.

Act it out

Some people like to **act out** their characters as it helps to work out who they are. Remember, writing is really just playing but with a pen so why not walk around being each of your characters in turn. Think about how they talk, how they walk. Let yourself get into the characters and let the characters get into you.

If you **practise** doing this, eventually, you'll find your characters doing all sorts of things you hadn't thought of.

I have just tried being the **Wizard-Farmer** whilst walking around my back garden and I found out that when he runs he bends his knees in a funny way and he sounds a little bit American.

What would your characters do if?

Here are some quick questions to ask about the characters in your story that will hopefully help you learn more about them.

Choose one character you'd like to include in your story and write answers to the questions below.

Character's name:

_____

What would they do if they were stuck in a lift with a bear?

_____

_____

_____

_____

_____

_____

What is their favourite type of cheese?

_____

_____

_____

_____

_____

What is the most embarrassing thing they have ever done?

_____

_____

_____

_____

_____

What colour is their hair?

_____

_____

_____

_____

_____

What's the bravest thing they have ever done?

_____

_____

_____

_____

_____

Who is their best friend?

_____

_____

_____

_____

Do they have any pets?

_____

_____

_____

_____

Answers into questions

Try the following exercise to help develop one of your characters more:

- Write down five things about yourself
- Turn these points into questions
- Ask these questions about your character

For example:

I am quite tall.
I like climbing mountains.
I'm afraid of sharks.
I went to school in England.
I'm allergic to nuts.

Then turn these things into the questions:

How tall are you?
What sporty activities do you like?
What are you afraid of?
Where did you go to school?
Do you have any allergies?

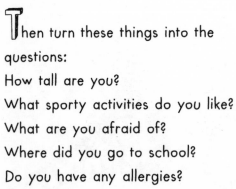

Now I can ask these same questions about Daphne the Milkmaid and the answers will hopefully help me learn more about my character.

Daphne is **very tall** for her age and is always banging her head on the roof of the barn.

Daphne likes playing **mini golf** with the cows.

Daphne has never met anything she is **afraid** of until her dad created the Marmalade Cow.

Daphne doesn't go to school because she is **too busy** milking cows. Her dad gives her old exercise books to read when the cows are asleep but they are the exercise books he had as a child and are full of all the wrong answers.

Daphne is **allergic** to dairy.

Now try this with your own characters.

Write down five things about yourself:

1 _____

_____

_____

2 _____

_____

_____

3 _____

_____

_____

4 _____

_____

_____

5 _____

_____

_____

Turn each point into a question:

1 _____

_____

_____

2 _____

_____

_____

3 _____

_____

_____

4 _____

_____

_____

5 _____

_____

_____

Now put these questions to your characters and see what you find out. Write what you discover below:

SETTING

A setting is a way of describing **where** your story takes place. It's usually best if your story takes place in the same world all the way through, although some stories, of course, have a **secret door** of some kind that takes you from one world to another.

My story of the Marmalade Cow is going to take place in a normal sort of British countryside. With mad characters like the ones I have thought of, it's probably a good idea to keep the setting fairly **normal.** So I'm going to have a normal town with a market and shops. There will also be some woods where something mysterious lives perhaps.

WELCOME TO
DULLSVILLE

TWINNED WITH
TERNE — FRANCE
STUMPF — GERMANY
ABURRIDO — SPAIN
NOIOSO — ITALY

What will be the **setting** for your story? It could be a city, a village, space, under the ground, in a land of dinosaurs, a jungle, a haunted house, the clouds?

Use the space below to describe where your story is going to be set:

Have a think about how your characters are going to fit into your setting. Are they going to feel at home? Or will they stand out as being in the wrong sort of place?

In my story I'm going to have farmers, milkmaids, shopkeepers and all sorts of people you might normally find in a normal rural place. But by putting a Wizard-Farmer into the mix, that might make things really **exciting**.

Play around with thinking of a character that doesn't quite fit in your setting but might make the whole thing more interesting.

Write a list of settings your characters could inhabit.
My Marmalade Cow, for example, could be in a story set on a farm,
time-travelling, in a scary monster story, or in a real-world-child-
goes-to-school kind of setting. It would be hilarious if you took
a marmalade cow to school with you!

Setting One:

Setting Two:

_____

_____

_____

_____

_____

_____

_____

Setting Three:

_____

_____

_____

_____

_____

_____

_____

Should you use a computer?

The idea of this book is that you use the blank pages throughout to write your story. But should you also use a **computer** for writing?

Computers are really good for **editing** and moving bits of text around. It's a lot quicker than having to write everything out again. You can also use computers to send the stories to other people really easily.

Some people write straight on to a computer. And I do that occasionally. But mainly I like to write things out in my **notebook** with a pen and then copy it up onto my computer. This might be because I am old-fashioned and old. Maybe you can go straight onto a computer or tablet or some other **digital device**.

But I really like watching the words come out of the pen and on to an actual piece of paper. Also, there is a really important difference between doing your first draft on paper compared

to digitally. If I write something
with a pen and paper and
I make a mistake, I will
then cross it out. It's
crossed out but it's
still there. Then,
the next day or a month
later or years later, if I'm
reading through my notebooks
I might see something that I crossed
out and realise that actually, the thing I
thought of was possibly something really interesting.

I thought it was a mistake at the time but now I can see
that it wasn't. If I did that same piece of writing on my laptop
and make the same mistake, I would then delete using the
backspace button. And then that mistake would disappear
forever. If I read that same document a month later, I wouldn't
be able to see what I had deleted and it would be forgotten
about **forever.**

Things you do not need to be a writer

We know what you need to be a writer but let's have a think about all the **stuff** that you don't need.

You do not need:

- A donkey
- A helicopter
- A special hat with 'I'm a brilliant writer' stitched on it in gold thread
- Protective clothing
- A drill
- Lucky pants
- An office

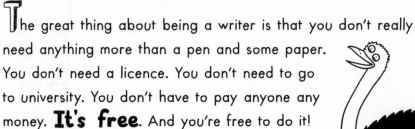

- Eight portions of chocolate cake
- Coffee
- TNT
- Magic writing slippers
- An inspirational ostrich
- An army of attack spiders you have trained to destroy anyone trying to distract you

The great thing about being a writer is that you don't really need anything more than a pen and some paper. You don't need a licence. You don't need to go to university. You don't have to pay anyone any money. **It's free**. And you're free to do it!

82

PLANNING

In this section you're going to **plan** your story. Remember, writing a story without planning it first is like going to school without any clothes on. It'll all go horribly **wrong**.

Use this space to write down your favourite idea from the ones you have come up with in the last section of this book. Don't worry about writing it as a proper story. No one else is going to see this. Just scribble stuff down.

The following pages look at three different ways of finding out more about your story.

The first one involves some **drawing**, the second one is about **writing** and the third one is about getting up and doing stuff. Do all three of them!

You might find that one of them works a lot better than the others. You might find that one of them doesn't really work for you at all. You might find that they are all brilliant! Whatever happens, one of them should be really **useful**.

Labels

The first thing that you need to do is write your idea at the top of a big blank page. Don't write a great long novel. Just describe your idea. Try and keep it to one medium-sized sentence, about as long as a shoelace. Here are some examples:

My cat learns how to do back-flips and joins the circus.

The Marmalade Cow takes over a zoo and builds an army of monkeys to rule the world.

Poppy is left at home with her baby brother and her parents disappear.

Next you will need to draw a picture. **Don't panic!** This book hasn't suddenly turned into an art lesson. You don't have to be good at drawing. In fact, it's probably better for this bit if you are not very good at drawing. (I'll explain why later.) These pictures never go into the finished book. Instead, the pictures are a way of getting to know your ideas better, before you start writing them properly in your story.

Imagine your idea is a **new friend**. This method is going to help you get to know your new friend a little better.

So now it's time to get on with it and draw a picture of your idea. Don't worry about making it perfect. It doesn't matter. Make sure you fill up the whole page. No mousey little pictures in the corner. If your idea involves a cat and you're thinking, 'I don't know how to draw a cat,' don't worry about it. Draw a **rubbish cat**.

And don't just draw exactly what's in your description of your idea. Add **details**: background trees, mountains, windows, curtains, camels, rainbows. Whatever seems to fit. Whatever feels to you like it should be in the picture. Don't worry about colouring it in and don't think too much about what it looks like.

Use the space below to write your idea and draw a picture of it.

No mousey little pictures!

You should now have written down a short sentence describing your idea and drawn a picture of it. I hope you're not too **proud** of it because the next thing you're going to do is ruin it!

I want you to label your picture. Label **everything!** Label the labels if you want to. Label the air between the things themselves if it makes you happy. Labels are the bridge between pictures and writing. And that's what we are trying to do with this technique. We are using the picture that we made to help us learn more about our idea and about what we are going to write.

If you have made any mistakes or drawn something by accident, then just label it by describing what it is and not what it was supposed to be. Write, 'funny-looking dog', or, 'my sister looks like she is floating', or, 'giant hat'. Label everything you see and make fun out of what you have drawn.

Giant hat

You should now have a picture of your idea, which you have covered in labels – something like this:

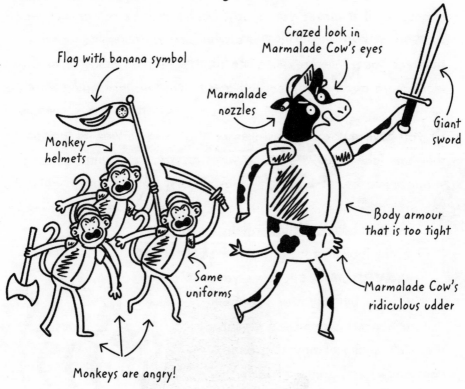

Flag with banana symbol

Crazed look in Marmalade Cow's eyes

Marmalade nozzles

Giant sword

Monkey helmets

Body armour that is too tight

Same uniforms

Marmalade Cow's ridiculous udder

Monkeys are angry!

The **next stage** is the really exciting bit.

You're going to stare at your labelled picture and try to look between the labels or behind them. Find the really interesting or **silly idea**, the unusual mistake. Try and find the bit that no one else but you could have thought of.

Is there a story in the floating sister? What would happen if your sister learned to fly? Would you be happy for her and go on adventures together? Or would you be jealous and try to steal her powers?

Is your story the tale of the funny-looking foot and the **hilarious adventures** it takes you on? Or maybe your story is about a bonkers pigeon – a pigeon that isn't afraid of anything and is constantly getting into all sorts of difficulties.

Looking back at my picture, I have noticed that there is a **mistake** with the army of monkeys. They're all wearing identical uniforms! This means that they are all the same type of army monkey and none of them will be in charge. Surely an army of monkeys wouldn't work very well like that. There might be some problems, which would make for an **interesting** story.

I've also noticed that the Marmalade Cow has nozzles in her ears!

Write your **new idea** down on the next page and have a look at it.

You might want to throw your first idea away because this one is **better**.

You might decide that your first idea was actually much **stronger** but this technique has helped you learn more about it.

There is no right or wrong answer to any of this. Whatever happened in your picture, between the labels and your mind, is **right** for you and your story.

Write your new idea here:

What sometimes happens is that you might find your **second idea** fits together with the first idea making a double-super idea. This is one of the best ways to make a really strong idea for stories. Two or more ideas combined together. Is there a way that you can use both of your ideas in the same story?

We're fantastic!

Write a better description for your story here:

My new and **improved** story looks like this:

A wizard-farmer creates a marmalade cow to provide marmalade for everyone but something goes wrong and the marmalade cow turns bad. She forms an army of monkeys who are all in charge of each other and tries to take over the world.

Detective

This is **another way** of getting to know your story before you start writing it. It's lots of fun and you get to be a detective!

Imagine a crime has been committed. Maybe someone has stolen a precious jewel. It's the detective's job to ask questions and find out who stole the jewel, why and how. He does this in lots of ways, including asking the suspects questions.

In the next section you are going to ask yourself some questions about your story. You can **dress up** as a detective if you want but it's not necessary.

The first thing to do is look again at the better **description** of your story. This is what you are going to start with. Mine looks like this:

The Marmalade Cow – who has nozzles in her ears – builds an army of monkeys to take over the world but makes the mistake of designing all their uniforms the same so none of them is in charge.

The **next task** is to write down three questions to ask about your idea.

They might be really easy or they might be really hard, but try and keep the questions simple — even if the answers are going to be **complicated**. It doesn't matter if you know the answer or not at the time you write the question but maybe have at least one that you don't know the answer to yet.

Here are my questions as an example:

- What are the nozzles in the Marmalade Cow's ears for? (I know the answer to this already.)

- Why does the Marmalade Cow want to take over the world? (I don't know the answer to this yet.)

- What happens when the monkeys try to be in charge? (I don't know the answer to this but I have half an idea in my head already.)

Use the space below to write **three questions** for your story.

That's your role as the detective, to know which questions to ask and then to ask them.

Remember, your job is to find out **more** about the idea.

1. _____

_____

_____

2. _____

_____

_____

3. _____

_____

_____

Your next job, of course, is to **answer** the questions.
Here are my answers:

The nozzles in the Marmalade Cow's ears are so that she can direct
her streams of marmalade with more power and accuracy.

The Marmalade Cow wants to take over the world because her heart
was broken when the daughter of the farmer that made her, left the
farm. She was so upset by this that she became bad and determined
to take her revenge on the world by covering everyone in marmalade.

The monkeys are used to having one monkey in charge of them,
telling them what to do. The Marmalade Cow makes the mistake of
giving them all the same uniform and so no one is in charge. They
all start giving each other orders and the result is chaos!

Use the space below to write the answers to your three questions:

1.

2.

3.

If you don't know what questions to ask or what the answers are then you had better start using your imagination and think of some! But if your **imagination** needs a little push then try using these examples as a starting point or to give yourself a little practice:

Why?

Why is he like that? What is her name? Why does that happen?

How does he react to this? What is one of those?

Why does he do that? Why does she think that?

In fact, if you can't think of any **intelligent** questions, just pretend you are three years old and keep asking 'why?' to all parts of your story.

Asking 'why?' will almost certainly **help you** find out more about your idea and help you plan your story.

What do you do if you **can't** think of any answers to your questions?

If you are having trouble with this, I think the thing to do is not to worry too much. You can always leave a bit blank. Maybe you'll work out the answer once you start writing your story. Maybe you'll never know. Maybe it isn't that important. But I do recommend that you **try.**

Some things are just a mystery.

Just close your eyes, ask yourself the question and see what pops into your head. I'm going to try this with a question about my Marmalade Cow story.

How does the farmer create the Marmalade Cow?

I don't know the answer to this so I'm going to close my eyes and ask the inside of my head ... I'm doing this now ... And my head tells me that he isn't just any farmer. He is a wizard-farmer and knows how to use **magic**.

He creates the Marmalade Cow by putting a spell on a normal cow and a jar of marmalade.

Remember, there are no right or wrong answers to any of your questions. Whatever you decide is the **right answer**.

Once you have written your answers, look at them carefully. Hopefully your answers will make you think of some more questions.

By now, these questions should really be getting into the **details** of your story. You might have three more questions. Or maybe even more!

Write down your other questions and answers below.

Here are my three questions, which came from my first set of answers.

1. What happens to people when marmalade from the Marmalade Cow's ears hits them?

2. Who is going to stop the Marmalade Cow from taking over the world?

3. Where did the Marmalade Cow get all of the monkeys from?

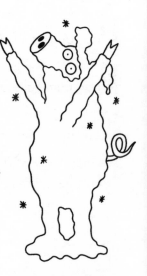

And my answers:

1. It is magic marmalade and it freezes anyone it touches until they are released.

2. The farmer's daughter who broke her heart is the only one that can stop her. Her name is Daphne.

3. The Marmalade Cow got her army of monkeys from an online site for bad guy supplies. It is called Bad-Guy-Bay.

You can probably see by now that asking questions about your idea and then answering them is a really good way to **plan** your story. This can go on and on for a very long time if you want it to. Keep going until one of these things happens:

You can't think of any more questions

You run out of paper

Your bum falls off

You think, 'Austrian Hiccups! I'm doing so much writing here, I might as well write the story!'

Whichever one of these things happens to you first, it's time to stop doing the detective method and start the final planning exercise ...

Playing around

Remember how we talked about getting ideas in the playground? When we are **playing** is when we are at our most creative and what authors do for a living is really just playing. The only difference is that they write it down.

Adults get funny looks when they run around pretending to be marmalade cows but you, however, can play as much as you want. You can use your playing to plan your story. You can be the characters in your story and **act out** the things that they do.

When I was a child I was brilliant at playing story games. Sometimes I would act out games with my friends, sometimes I would play with my little brother and tell him what I wanted him to say. Often we would make puppets out of cardboard and do puppet shows of my stories.

Loads of times though, I would play stories on my own with just some toy figures. I would use them as the characters in my story and I loved seeing my figures going on adventures that I had created.

By doing this I became **really good** at playing writing games inside my head that no one else could see.

When I was walking to school I would look like any other child but in my head I would be shooting space ships with lasers or piloting a submarine to the bottom of the sea. It might have looked like I was in the back of the car on my way to visit Auntie Heather, but in my **imagination** I was on a secret mission to recover the jewellery of a princess disguised as our pet dog.

So what you're going to do next is put this book down and **play!**

It doesn't matter how you do it or who you do it with. Just play your story. Be your characters. **Act out** the things you want them to do and have fun!

You don't have to stick to what you've been writing about. In fact, it's probably best if you don't. **Go further** with your story. See where the game takes you. Play with the characters and let the characters lead you and shape the game.

SCRUB THE POOP DECK!

THE SHAPE OF YOUR STORY

You have almost certainly come across the idea of the **Story Mountain** before. Your teacher probably drew a picture of a mountain on the board and explained how a story starts at one end and then builds up, getting more and more exciting and then goes down the other side as everything gets sorted out and the story ends.

This is a brilliant way of looking at the **structure** of your story.

But ... Even though I love climbing mountains, I'm not sure that a mountain is the best sort of metaphor for your story. Here are some reasons why ...

1. Climbing mountains is hard work. Writing stories is **fun**. It shouldn't be hard.

2. When you are climbing a mountain there is a danger you might fall off and hurt yourself. I don't think anyone has ever hurt themselves whilst writing a story, although I did once accidentally poke myself in the eye with my pen.

3. If it rains when you are climbing a mountain, you get wet. If it rains when you are writing a story you go inside and watch the raindrops rolling down the window.

4. Usually when you climb a mountain you don't go up one side and down the other. If you do that you'll be somewhere else. Climbing a mountain and going down the opposite side is a sure way to

accidentally end up in another country by mistake. When you climb a mountain in real life you tend to end up back where you started, because that is where your tent is. Some stories do finish where they started but they are usually a **bit weird**. Most stories start in one place and then take the reader on a wonderful **journey** to somewhere else.

For all of these reasons I have decided to invent my own way of structuring a story and I call it ...

The Story Rainbow

Rainbows are a much better **metaphor** for the **shape** of a story, and here are a few reasons why.

1. Rainbows are awesome. You have to climb a mountain but you can just ride a rainbow like you would a stripy flying unicorn dragon. Rainbows are **magical** and so are stories.

2. Rainbows are made up of different colours. Stories are made up of **different colours** too. The colours are the characters, the plot, the setting, the style and the words.

3. Rainbows are slightly **different** for everyone that sees them. I don't know the exact science behind it but apparently every time you see a rainbow it is your rainbow and the rainbow

The Problem

Getting On With It

The Beginning

that anyone else is seeing is their rainbow. The book that you are about to write is your book. Only you can see it the way that it is and **only you** can write it the way that you are going to write it.

4. The Inspiration Elf lives at the **end** of the rainbow. I know this because it just told me so.

The **Story Rainbow** is divided into five sections like in this illustration.

The Beginning

Getting On With It

The Problem

Sorting It Out

The End

The **Beginning** of your story is where you introduce your main character, describe them a bit and explain things like where they live and who they are. You might also write about the setting of the story and show the reader what sort of book it is.

The **Getting On With It** section is where you actually start the story. You might start this bit with something like ... One day ... That weekend ... The next morning ...

The **Problem** section of the rainbow is the part where some conflict has turned up and things start to get really exciting. Maybe it's a **baddie**. Maybe it's a challenge or a quest. Maybe someone is lost or trapped. It all depends on your story. A story without any problems can be quite boring so make sure yours has a fantastic problem in the middle.

The **Sorting It Out** part of your story rainbow is when they solve the problem. Your characters escape from the monster, find the magic sword or do whatever is relevant to your story.

The **End** is when they all have a nice cup of tea and go to bed. Or wander off into the sunset. Or decide that they are now a gang and will continue fighting bad guys until the galaxy is safe. Or switch off their torch, go to sleep and dream their day all over again.

There is no reason why you must make a story rainbow. Lots of stories don't have this shape. You might want to write a story that has a different shape and that's **okay**. This is your book, not mine.

You might choose to start your story with the problem bit and then go **backwards** to explain who everyone is and how they got there.

MAIN CHARACTER

You might not want to solve the problem at all. Maybe you just want everything to **explode** and that's the end of your story.

Maybe your story doesn't end. Maybe it just **keeps going** round and round in circles. Maybe your story is two rainbows that come together at the end or the middle or start off together, split up and then come back again.

Maybe you have found your own way of **structuring** a story that no one else has thought of yet. Good. Write it. Show it to people. It's your story. It's your rainbow. Only you can see it the way you are seeing it.

BUT if you want to use the story rainbow shape then that's okay too. If you're not sure how to shape your story, take a look at the story rainbow below as an example.

Daphne the Milkmaid

The Beginning: Daphne was a milkmaid who was allergic to milk.

Getting On With It: One day she was given the job of milking the cows.

The Problem: But the milk got in her eyes and she couldn't see!

Sorting It Out: Fortunately a friendly otter came along who wiped the milk out of her eyes with his super-absorbent tail and helped Daphne milk the cows in record time.

The End: She won a medal and was given a year's supply of soya milk that she wasn't allergic to.

Now try and write your own Story Rainbow using one of your story ideas.

The Beginning:

_____

_____

_____

_____

_____

_____

Getting On With It:

_____

_____

_____

_____

_____

_____

The Problem:

_____

_____

_____

_____

Sorting It Out:

_____

_____

_____

_____

The End:

_____

_____

_____

_____

If you have another story idea then you can write
a Story Rainbow for that one too:

The Beginning:

Getting On With It:

The Problem:

Sorting It Out:

The End:

125

GET READY TO WRITE

You are now nearly **ready** to start writing your own funny story. But what if you're not? What can you do about it?

Go right back to the beginning of the planning section and read through all of your notes and exercises. Have another look at the picture you covered in labels. Read through the questions you asked yourself as a detective. Think about the games you played when you were pretending to be the characters from your story.

After you've done all of this you should feel a little bit more ready to get started. But even if you don't, why don't you start writing anyway? Maybe you **don't need** to feel ready to be ready.

Where's my magic slippers?

Just start writing.

Free writing

Sometimes it can be good to clear out your brain pipes before writing a story. Have a go at some **'free writing'** to help you get started. Time yourself for ten minutes and write absolutely anything and everything that comes into your head!

Don't worry about spelling or grammar – just keep writing! The result? Probably a lot of **nonsense** but the inside of your head will be lovely and clean!

Free drawing

If you still feel like your brain pipes have a bit of dust covering them then why not try some **free drawing?**

Get a pen and draw the first thing that comes in to your head! If you need some help then pick three things from the words below to inspire you:

- My horrible
- My favourite
- The blue
- A boring
- Donkey
- Allen

- Teacher
- Cat
- Flew a plane
- Invented underwear
- Turned into a cake
- Is a superhero

More space for free drawing:

You're ready to start!

Some people say that starting with that first blank page can be scary. It's not scary. It's **exciting**. There is nothing to be scared of. You can't get this wrong.

This is your first story and it is going to be the **best story** you have ever written.

It might be best to use a pencil so you can rub things out and change them along the way. You can always write it out in pen later.

There is no wrong story for you to write. You can only write the **right story**. You have all those ideas and characters and things that are going to happen inside your brain and in your heart. So just let them out. You can spend ages reading books and watching videos about swimming but eventually if you want to learn to swim you need to get in the water. It's now time to take a deep breath and **dive in**.

And you won't be on your own! I've written various things to help you as you go along. So just imagine I'm watching over you from the corner of the ceiling like a **ninja-author!**

I can't think of the right words.

Then you need to find some more words!

The natural habitat of words is books – that's where they live. Try reading some books and you'll uncover new words and new ways of using them. The more you read the better your writing will become. Libraries are a great place to start to find new books – before you know it you'll know more words than the dictionary!

I found all the words.

> I'm worried that what I'm writing is rubbish.

> Sometimes we can all get a bit worried about our writing. But writing should be fun! I've answered some worries below to help you on your way to becoming an awesome author.
>
> All authors get that feeling at one time or another. You just have to tell yourself to stop having such silly thoughts! Of course it isn't rubbish. It's a new story that no one but you could have thought of. How can that be anything but brilliant? Are you sure?

My writing isn't as good as I thought it was going to be.

There might be some bits which aren't as good as you imagined but I bet there are also lots of bits which are even better! And lots of bits that you didn't even know were going to be there. Your story is probably better than you think but you're just looking at it from the wrong direction. Why not read what you have written so far to someone who will listen. Even if you know you can do better, a story that you have written is always better than a story that you haven't written.

My hand hurts after a while.

You might need to change the way you hold your pencil. Or maybe you're holding it too tightly. You don't need to hold the pencil too hard – just be gentle and every now and again, put the pencil down and wiggle your fingers around.

I'm fed up of writing.

Well go and do something else then! Run around the garden, do the washing-up, help your grown-ups with the shopping – just take a break and come back to writing your book when you're ready.

My handwriting
is terrible.

So is mine! When I'm writing
I can't concentrate on the story
and be neat at the same time.
I can, however, write nicely if
I try hard enough. Try writing
without worrying about your
handwriting. Do this in pencil and
then when you've finished, you
can rub it out and write it out
again in your best handwriting.

Sometimes my brain is thinking of the words faster than my hand can write them down. My thoughts get so far ahead of my writing that I forget bits.

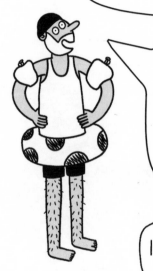

This happens to lots of authors. I think the trick is not to worry too much. Worrying will cause you to forget what you want to say. Relaxing will help you remember. Some authors also write bullet points of their story so they can jot everything down quickly and then come back to it and add more later.

I remember!

Nonsense Poem

Take a **break** from writing your story for a moment and on the opposite page write a piece of nonsense just for fun. Below are a few opening lines to help you:

- I like avocados but I can't tell you why.

- My sister plays the Welsh Trombone.

- If you really, really want to jump inside my planet ...

- Cows are nice. Cows are lovely.

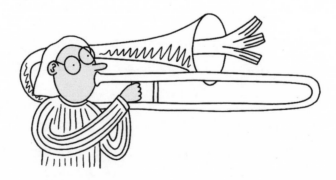

Keeping On Track

You're probably somewhere in the **middle** of your story by now. The middle is usually the hardest bit to write. The beginning is lots of fun because you're starting a new thing and it's really exciting. The end is quite easy because you've nearly finished and you know that you only have to keep going for a little bit more and you'll have done it!

So **how** do you get through the difficult middle bit? Apart from just rolling up your sleeves and carrying on, the following tips are also **useful** to keep you going:

- Count how many words you have written so far

- Do some star jumps

- Find a pet, brother, sister or teddy and tickle them

- Draw a picture

- Take your clothes off, turn them inside out and put them back on again

People To Help

At some point you might want to **share** your story with some other people. Maybe if you're a bit stuck and you aren't sure what's going to happen next. Or maybe if you're not sure what you've written so far is any good.

Choose someone **carefully** and ask them if they can help you. It might be a good idea to read them a bit or maybe just to tell them about the story you are writing.

STOP

30

Finding A Quiet Place

It's good to have somewhere nice and quiet to write, somewhere that's just **your space**.

Your **bedroom** might be a good place or maybe the bottom of the **garden**.

However, some authors write in cafés where there is lots of noise around them, so it doesn't have to be silent. If you try writing in odd places like the back of the car, the playground, or on trains, you will slowly learn how to **concentrate** anywhere!

Juxtaposition Word Game

Why not take a break from writing your story for a minute and try this little **word game**.

Start by picking a word – it can be any word at all. For example, Jammy.

Then pick another word that could go with it. For example, Sandwich.

This makes: **Jammy Sandwich**.

Next take your new word and think of another word that goes with it. For example: **Sandwich Adventure**.

Adventure Penguin Penguin Soup

Soup Disaster Disaster Creator

Go on for as long as you like and then look back at your list of words. Is there a **little idea** in there? When you have finished this, get back to writing your own story!

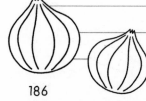

This is the last page of the book.

Congratulations on making it this far.

You get to see a picture of a naked Marmalade Cow!

CLASSIFIED!

But seriously, if you have followed the suggestions in this book and written your own story, then not only will you have finished **READING** my funny book, you will have finished **WRITING** your own funny story.

This is incredible.

Most people (including grown-ups) don't know how to sit down and write a whole story from start to finish. They just don't. **YOU DO.**

So now you really are a **writer**. What are you going to write next?